NEW DAY NEW WAY

28 DAYS

TO A HAPPIER, HEALTHIER YOU

DR HEIDI TEMPEST

NewU Journals

The Oleander Press
16 Orchard Street
Cambridge
CB1 1JT

www.oleanderpress.com

© 2017
The right of Dr Heidi Tempest to be identified as the author of this work
has been asserted in accordance with the Copyright, Designs and Patents
Act 1988.
Designed and typeset by Ayshea Carter
Images by Freepik

A CIP catalogue record for the book is available from the British Library.
ISBN: 978-1-9999004-0-3

CONTENTS

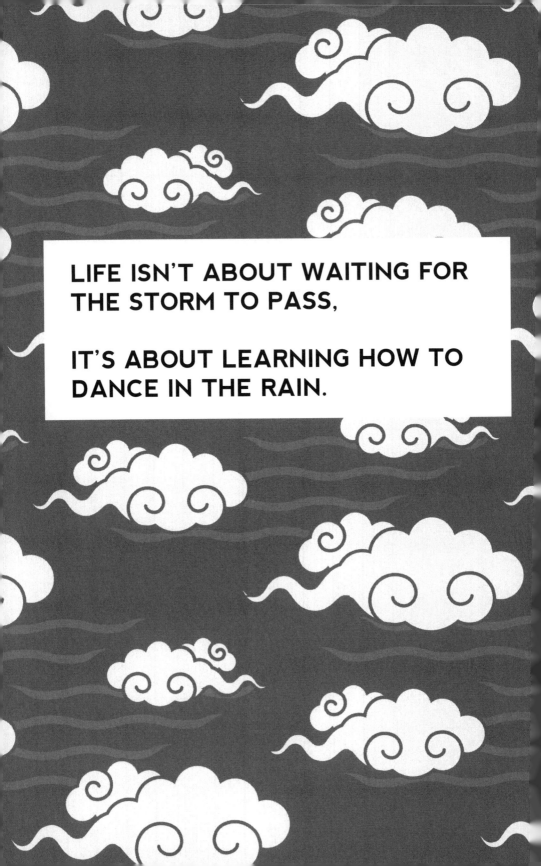

LIFE ISN'T ABOUT WAITING FOR THE STORM TO PASS,

IT'S ABOUT LEARNING HOW TO DANCE IN THE RAIN.

HAVE YOU EVER FELT THAT YOU'VE LOST YOUR MOJO?

NEEDED HELP REACHING A GOAL OR EVEN STARTING A PROJECT?

OR PERHAPS YOU'RE PREPARING FOR A BIG OCCASION OR RECOVERING FROM A LIFE-CHANGING EVENT?

If so, this wellbeing journal could be just what you need - by providing the structure, timetable and routine to enable you to fulfill your aims and reach your goals. Today's world is a kaleidoscope of stresses that can easily overcome even the most level-headed of us. When this happens we all need a method for calming and re-centering ourselves so that we can go back to enjoying the life we've worked hard to achieve. This journal will help you get there - in a realistic and manageable timeframe.

The main emphasis of the journal is to allow you to have fun whilst running through the exercises. If you enjoy yourself, you'll be a lot more likely to stick to the plan and gain your confidence faster. So enjoy yourself!

The journal is spilt into sections which you can work through but the 28 day planner at the back can be used alongside these - or on its own if you prefer to create your own routine.

The first section is Self-awareness and Goal Setting. The aim here is to allow you to define your current situation and to use that as a foundation for the new you that you're going to build. Here you'll be able to consider your aims for the month and to picture the place you want to be by then. Defining goals - both small and large - is very useful for building confidence. Your imagination is the only limit here - be sure to include crazy, fun or just plain silly ideas. Stimulating the creative side of your brain has been shown to be instrumental in helping solve more difficult issues - and what could be bigger or more important than your own life and the happiness you derive from it?

The second section is Exercise - and is self-explanatory. The aim here is to come up with ideas to get you moving. There are now countless studies that show how vital exercise is to your health - both physical and mental. You may not be sporty - but there are hundreds of different ways to get the benefits from physical exertion that aren't laborious or monotonous. We're certainly not talking about doing the hoovering!

The third section is your 'Get Back on Track' chapter. This is for resetting your balance on the more difficult days you may have. Or for when you're just in need of a positive boost. It is chock-full of useful exercises too.

For **the final section** is your **Daily Planner**. The structured format of the Planner allows you to easily record your progress and building a momentum will help you on your way to the new you. There are also weekly reflection pages to emphasise your results.

You'll see large thought boxes throughout the journal - use these to write down your thoughts, ideas and answers to the exercises you're working on. Whenever you see a small progress box, make sure you tick it to show you've completed that assignment - it's important to visualise your progress and positively reinforce your achievements!

Feel free to use the journal in any way you like. Different parts will inspire different people; we are all different, after all, and that's what interests and excites us as social creatures - no one is exactly the same.

Also make sure to doodle, design and jot down your thoughts anywhere you like in the journal. Feel free to decorate and colour any of the designs - they're there to bring everyday mindfulness, calm and inspiration whenever and wherever you like.

ENJOY!!

SELF-AWARENESS

AND

GOAL SETTING

What parts of your life are you happy with and which need improvement? You might find this life star overleaf helpful in thinking about the different parts of your life.

. . . .

. . . .

. . . .

. . . .

. . . .

DOODLE AREA

You might find this life star helpful to think about the different parts of your life.

HEALTH

FUN
&
RECREATION

PERSONAL
DEVELOPMENT

FINANCES

CAREER

ENVIRONMENT

SLEEP
&
RELAXATION

LOVE
&
RELATIONSHIPS

WHAT DO YOU THINK YOUR STRENGTHS ARE?

. . . .

. . . .

It can also be very helpful to ask close friends or relatives to write down what they think your strengths are. Often you'll find yourself pleasantly surprised.

OTHER PEOPLE'S THOUGHTS ON YOUR STRENGTHS

. . . .

. . . .

START ADDING COLOUR TO YOUR LIFE!

HOW WOULD YOU LIKE YOUR LIFE TO LOOK?

Draw anything that symbolises how you see your life at present. Then on the other page, draw what you would like to see. The pictures can be as silly or exuberant as you like – it's just a simple but effective way of visualising your journey and destination.

What steps can you take to progress from the present to your desired future picture?

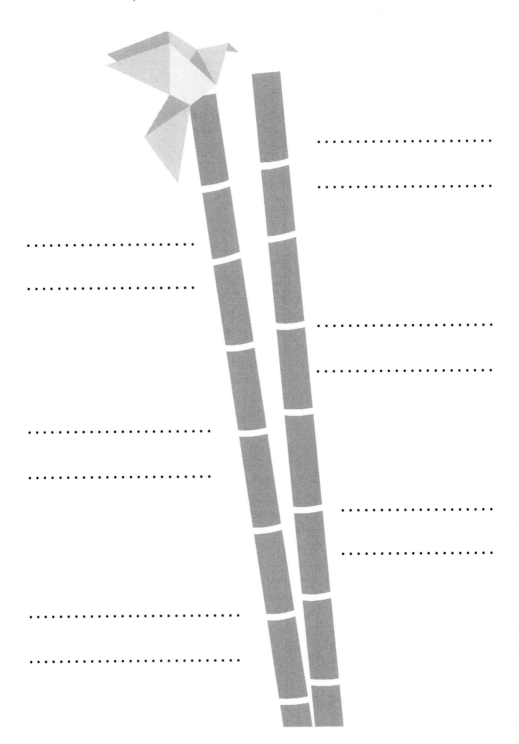

WHO ARE THE PEOPLE THAT BRING LIGHT INTO YOUR LIFE?

We all have different strengths. Write down your 'go to' people for different aspects of your life.

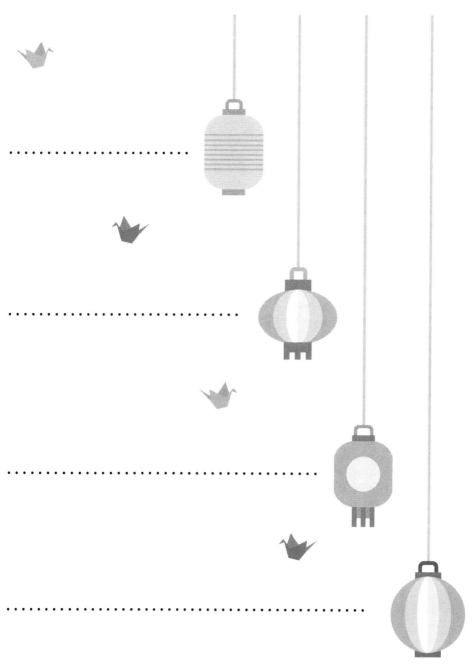

....

....

....

....

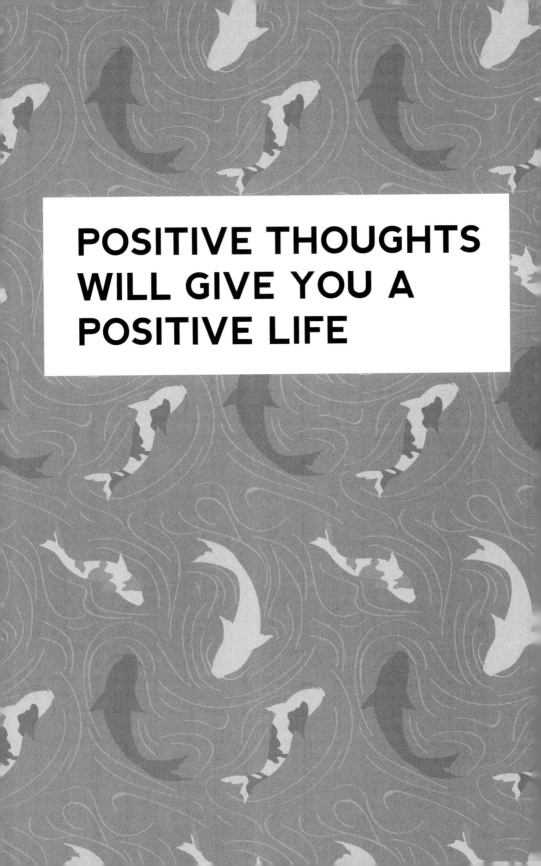

POSITIVE THOUGHTS WILL GIVE YOU A POSITIVE LIFE

MY SANCTUARY

Finding your own special place, your sanctuary, is important. It could be a favourite place, a quiet room or even the bath. It needn't even be real - think of an imaginary location – a beach of dreams, a mountain top, a forest waterfall – anywhere you can visit in your mind whenever you close your eyes and focus. A real place is probably easier for most people but both are equally helpful in taking you away from everyday life for a while.

TO LOVE SOMEONE YOU HAVE TO LOVE YOURSELF.

Think of three things you like about yourself.

1

2

3

*COLOUR US IN WHILE
YOU THINK*

WHAT IS YOUR MAIN GOAL FOR THE NEXT 4 WEEKS?

WHAT ARE YOUR OTHER GOALS FOR THIS JOURNEY?

EXERCISE

THE SCIENTIFIC STUDIES KEEP DEMONSTRATING THAT EXERCISE IS ONE OF THE BEST MEDICINES YOU CAN BENEFIT FROM.

There's no getting away from it - exercise is vital for mind, body and soul and is important as part of a regular daily routine. By building frequent exercise into your daily life you'll feel happier and more confident whilst looking better. This is not a tall order - you won't even notice you're exercising if you make it more fun.

THE RECOMMENDED MINIMUM DAILY EXERCISE HAS BEEN SUGGESTED AS **10,000** STEPS

Most smartphones have apps that can count steps and there are also affordable trackers available as well as the very popular 'fitbit' products.

Do try to vary the forms of exercise though - cardio one day, toning another perhaps.

THOUGHTS:

Are there any sports that you
have ever wanted to try? . . . .

Think of a sport you enjoy. You
don't have to be good at it! . . . .

Do you prefer individual/team
sports? . . . .

Any local clubs? . . . .

IDEAS

You can use these pages to devise your own exercise regime so you can add them to your daily routine.
You can have different ones for different days of the week depending on your commitments. You can have a rest day (or two) as well.

LIGHT EXERCISE

eg Walk the dog

....

....

....

....

SPORTS

eg Tennis

....

....

....

....

HARDER EXERCISE

eg Bike ride

....

....

....

OTHER

eg Yoga

....

....

....

Which days will you be able to do them?

MONDAY	EXERCISE

TUESDAY	EXERCISE

WEDNESDAY	EXERCISE

THURSDAY	EXERCISE

FRIDAY	EXERCISE

SATURDAY	EXERCISE

SUNDAY	EXERCISE

There is also a fitness progress page so you can document
your possible goals (weekly weights/steps
or waist measurement etc.).

PLANNED FITNESS
REGIME FOR WEEK 1

| DAY 1 | EXERCISE |

| DAY 2 | EXERCISE |

| DAY 3 | EXERCISE |

| DAY 4 | EXERCISE |

| DAY 5 | EXERCISE |

| DAY 6 | EXERCISE |

| DAY 7 | EXERCISE |

STEPS / MILES	CALORIES		WATER

STEPS / MILES	CALORIES		WATER

STEPS / MILES	CALORIES		WATER

STEPS / MILES	CALORIES		WATER

STEPS / MILES	CALORIES		WATER

STEPS / MILES	CALORIES		WATER

STEPS / MILES	CALORIES		WATER

PLANNED FITNESS REGIME FOR WEEK 2

DAY 1	EXERCISE

DAY 2	EXERCISE

DAY 3	EXERCISE

DAY 4	EXERCISE

DAY 5	EXERCISE

DAY 6	EXERCISE

DAY 7	EXERCISE

STEPS / MILES	CALORIES

WATER

STEPS / MILES	CALORIES

WATER

STEPS / MILES	CALORIES

WATER

STEPS / MILES	CALORIES

WATER

STEPS / MILES	CALORIES

WATER

STEPS / MILES	CALORIES

WATER

STEPS / MILES	CALORIES

WATER

PLANNED FITNESS REGIME FOR WEEK 3

DAY 1	EXERCISE

DAY 2	EXERCISE

DAY 3	EXERCISE

DAY 4	EXERCISE

DAY 5	EXERCISE

DAY 6	EXERCISE

DAY 7	EXERCISE

STEPS / MILES	CALORIES		WATER

STEPS / MILES	CALORIES		WATER

STEPS / MILES	CALORIES		WATER

STEPS / MILES	CALORIES		WATER

STEPS / MILES	CALORIES		WATER

STEPS / MILES	CALORIES		WATER

STEPS / MILES	CALORIES		WATER

PLANNED FITNESS REGIME FOR WEEK 4

DAY 1   EXERCISE

DAY 2   EXERCISE

DAY 3   EXERCISE

DAY 4   EXERCISE

DAY 5   EXERCISE

DAY 6   EXERCISE

DAY 7   EXERCISE

STEPS / MILES	CALORIES

WATER

STEPS / MILES	CALORIES

WATER

STEPS / MILES	CALORIES

WATER

STEPS / MILES	CALORIES

WATER

STEPS / MILES	CALORIES

WATER

STEPS / MILES	CALORIES

WATER

STEPS / MILES	CALORIES

WATER

FITNESS PROGRESS

Think of how you can track your progress by different goals, eg weight, total steps, waist.

WEEK 1	WEEK 2

WEEK 3

WEEK 4

SMILE

SOMETIMES YOUR JOY IS THE SOURCE OF YOUR SMILE, BUT SOMETIMES YOUR SMILE CAN BE THE SOURCE OF YOUR JOY.

THICH NHAT HANH

HEALTHY EATING IS VERY IMPORTANT.
Think of three simple things you could do to improve on this.

1

2

3

FUN PART

HOW CAN YOU REWARD YOURSELF WITH WEEKLY TREATS?

WEEK 1

WEEK 2

WEEK 3

WEEK 4

◯ **TRY SOMETHING NEW** ◯

◯ **BE CREATIVE** ◯

◯ **DO SOMETHING NICE** ◯

IDEAS

SIMPLE/ACHIEVABLE	MORE CHALLENGING

GET BACK
ON TRACK

All great journeys are serious undertakings and we will all have days where we need a boost of positivity and inspiration. This section is for you to turn to in those moments and includes easy methods and exercises to help you back on track and on the way to achieving your goals.

DON'T BE HARD ON YOURSELF

JUST GET BACK TO IT!

YOU CAN'T CHANGE THE PAST...

BUT YOU CAN CHANGE YOUR FUTURE!

HOPE IS THE ONLY
THING STRONGER
THAN FEAR

It is possible
I can do this
I love the challenge
I have the strength
I believe in myself
I will do it
I will do it now

POSITIVE BOX
Write or draw a positive moment or experience

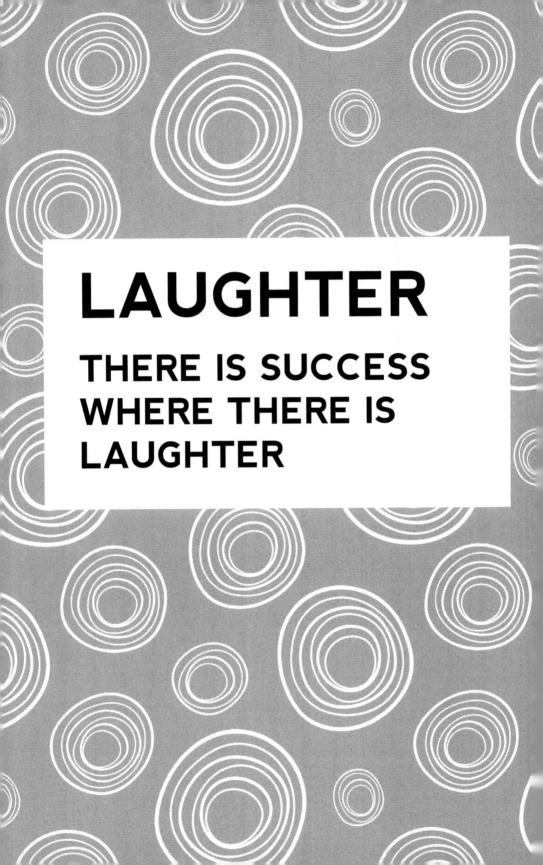

LAUGHTER

THERE IS SUCCESS WHERE THERE IS LAUGHTER

Think of things that make you laugh.

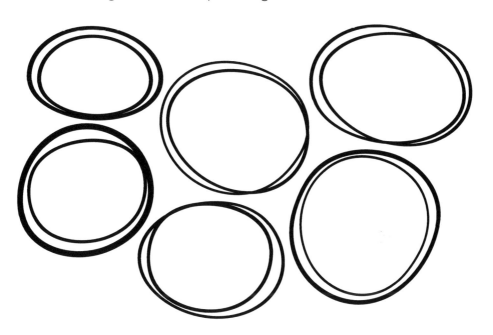

Think of previous funny experiences.

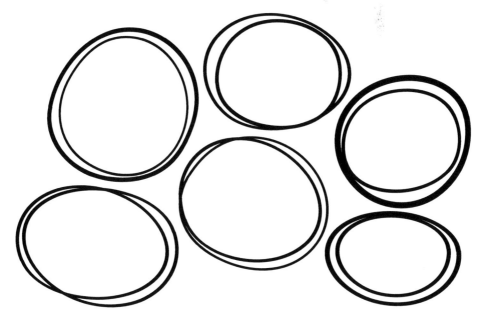

BE NOT AFRAID OF
GOING SLOWLY,
BE AFRAID OF
STANDING STILL.

Think of things that make you smile and give you joy

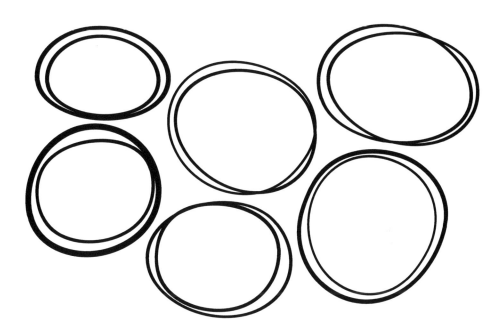

Think of your favourite songs or pieces of music that inspire and uplift you.

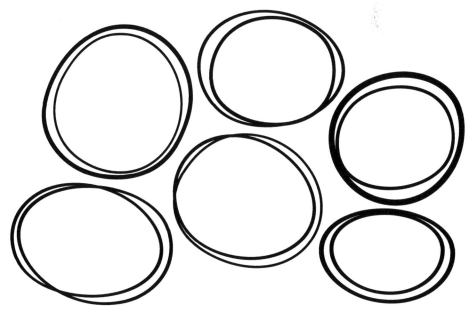

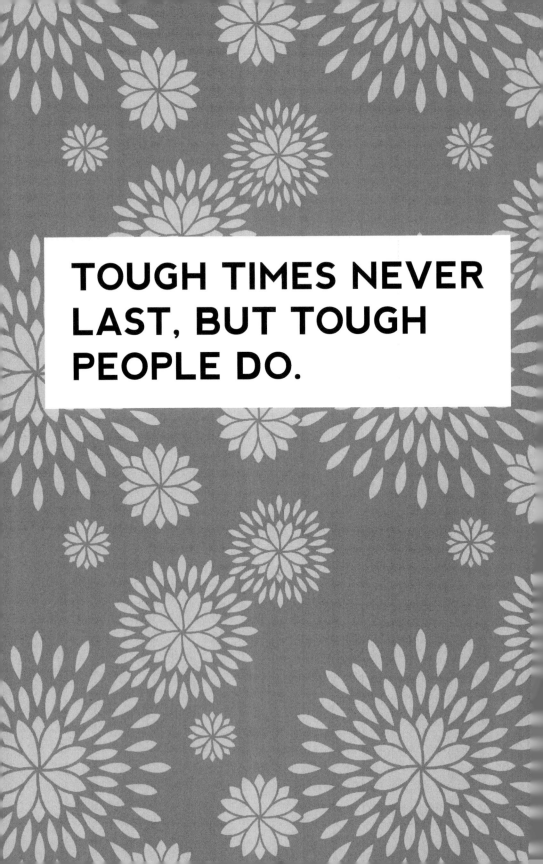

TOUGH TIMES NEVER LAST, BUT TOUGH PEOPLE DO.

Read aloud to boost your confidence and self esteem.

I believe in myself

I am truly awesome

I am stronger than I think

I can and I will, watch me

I will never give up

I will learn from experience

I love being me

I love life

I love my life

I am motivated

Write your own list of personal affirmations.

-
-
-
-
-
-
-
-

MY PAGE OF HAPPY MEMORIES

(draw or write)

INSTANT STRESS BUSTER

TAKE A FEW DEEP BREATHS

RELAX
FOREHEAD

RELAX
SHOULDERS

RELAX
JAW

RELAX
HANDS
AND
WRISTS

YOUR OWN STRESS BUSTERS

Mindfulness meditation has many benefits, including reducing depression and pain, increasing attention span and creativity whilst unbiasing the mind.

Although mindfulness is very popular, many people find it difficult and time consuming.
Start with easier exercises and proceed at your own pace.

A MINDFULNESS EXERCISE

- Just stop for a moment

- Be in the present

- Sit or lay comfortably

- Close your eyes

- Breathe in slowly and feel the air coming through your nose

- Breathe out slowly and feel the air going out of your mouth

- Focus your mind behind the mid-point of your forehead

- When you notice background sounds or distracting thoughts - let them go.

- Bring your focus back to that central point behind your forehead.

- Try this for 2 minutes and build up

RELAX AT YOUR DESK STRETCHES

People are sitting at their desks for ever-longer periods today, frequently resulting in them becoming tense. This in turn causes posture problems and pain.

Here are a few stretches you can do:

- Stand up and sit down without using your hands

- Shrug your shoulders to release your neck and shoulders

- Loosen the hands with air circles

- Stretch out your spine by sitting up straight as if being lifted by a string attached to the top of your head. Now stretch your arms overhead and interlock your fingers

- Stretch your legs out in front of you, then flex and point your toes 5 times

WORDSEARCH

```
U E O T R E T H G U A L Z Y I
E V V N R Y J L R R E X E P N
T S U S R S T F E H V T X P X
Q F L T P R E A Y C I S P A N
O T F A A E D P T T L I O H D
L I S R L I D J P E A N S D X
T M U T T H T R S R N G I I L
R E C L H T A Z O T H C T S N
Q R C I I L E E V S S D I W R
I F E K W A R C O P E L V I A
G G E E H E G C L T M S E R E
A A D B P H N A I A L N A E L
R E F O Y L Y C E O N Y J D P
M T H D B Z X R V N I W X R B
X K V W A E D E Q D D C Q O H
```

START	EXCITED	COPE
LIKE	WIN	NEW
LOVE	DREAM	READ
HOPE	SLEEP	LEARN
POSITIVE	GREAT	TRY
FUN	ME	FIT
PLAY	ALIVE	SUCCEED
LAUGHTER	TIME	HEALTHIER
STRETCH	ORDER	HAPPY
SING	FEEL	

SLEEP

GET BACK ON TRACK

Good quality/better sleep can help you get back on track.

The importance of sleep is often underestimated.
We regularly compromise on the time we leave for sleep - our ever-busier lives mean we try to get by on the bare minimum. Allowing extra time for sleep will soon have you feeling calmer, happier and more confident.

Clearing and/or rearranging your bedroom to make a relaxing, comfortable sleep environment will go a long way to helping you achieve better sleep.

The National Sleep Society recommends healthy sleep tips such as:

- **Stick to a sleep schedule - even at weekends**

- **Practice a relaxing bedtime ritual**

- **Create a good sleep environment**

- **Wind down before sleep and avoid electronics (yes! that does mean no tablets or phones)**

MOTIVATING METHODS
TO ACHIEVE YOUR GOALS

If you need a bit of motivation you can try different methods to achieve your goals.

DEVELOPMENT LADDER
ACHIEVE A POSITIVE MINDSET FOR CLIMBING IN THE RIGHT DIRECTION, HOWEVER BIG YOUR GOALS

PROGRESS LINES
HELPS BETTER VISUALISATION OF YOUR PROGRESS

DECLUTTERING
YOUR HOME OR WORKSPACE

GETTING YOUR HOME/ROOM IN MORE ORDER

This can sometimes be a big task, especially in a busy household. Just tidying a drawer can give you a great sense of satisfaction.

Even something as simple as this becomes significant in allowing you to feel you have more control over your life. Establishing this allows you another way of getting back on track.

THE DEVELOPMENT LADDER

Write each small task achieved on this ladder, starting from the bottom.

COLOUR THIS IN IF YOU HAVE TIME

You can use the organisational ladder for large projects - work, revision - whatever you want. Have rewards along the way as you reach certain points.

BE CREATIVE

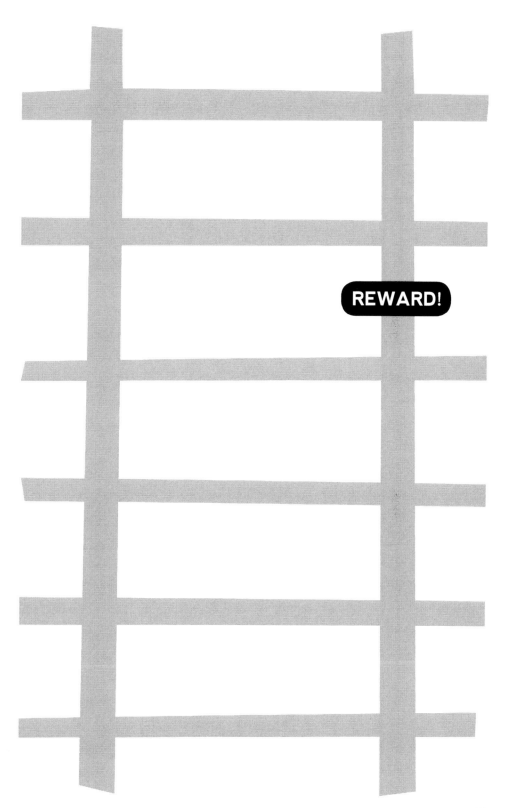

PROGRESS LINES

Joined Weight Watchers   Joined a gym

Weight loss ——————|——————————————|——————

GET BACK ON TRACK

This simple exercise allows you to illustrate the progress you've already made whilst also giving you the opportunity to visualise the pathway you're taking to achieve your goals.

Enrolled in
exercise class

THOUGHTS

THOUGHTS

THOUGHTS

THOUGHTS

THOUGHTS

THOUGHTS

THOUGHTS

THOUGHTS

THOUGHTS

THOUGHTS

HERE'S WHERE WE START TO
TURN YOUR LIFE AROUND

MY DAILY
PLANNER

I FEEL EXCITED FOR THE DAY

HAVING A DAILY PLAN WILL HELP YOU ACHIEVE YOUR GOALS

IN YOUR DAILY PLAN TRY TO INCORPORATE:

DAILY VISUALISATION

A good time to do this is when you first get up in the morning - maybe while still dozing, or perhaps while brushing your teeth or preparing breakfast. It doesn't really matter when you do it (and you can even use the picture you drew before) but by performing the daily visualisation now, you'll be starting the day with the best possible, positive mindset.

PERSONAL DEVELOPMENT

Life is enriched by continual learning and we can make sure we learn something new every day. Looking up information on the internet is something we can all do but you could also watch a TED talk, do a puzzle, start learning a new language or a musical instrument. There are a multitude of opportunities to stimulate your brain and the benefits will be just as plentiful. Of course, the main aim is to enjoy it.

RELAXATION

This is as important as working hard. Functioning under a constant burden of stress is like trying to fly an airplane with the wheels down and the flaps fully extended. The greater drag and resistance results in much of your energy being wasted. Mindfulness is also very good for overcoming this (*Get Back on Track* section).

PERSONAL AFFIRMATION

To keep your self-confidence high, do personal affirmations every day. There are examples in the *Get Back on Track* section.

HELPING OTHERS

Doing something for others has been shown to increase your own levels of happiness.

EXERCISE AND STRETCHES

You will have hopefully done your exercise programme in Section Two, and there are examples of stretches you can do at your desk in the *Get Back on Track* section.

FUN AND EXCITEMENT

The key to finding lots of fun and excitement in life is not just in the obvious but in the small things as well. Seeing the countryside, smelling beautiful flowers, tasting good food, hearing great music. Try to excite all your senses.

BE GRATEFUL

Think of the things you are grateful for each day before you go to sleep. This gratitude will bring you peace and create the best state of mind before sleeping.

PLEASANT DREAMS!

LIFE'S A JOURNEY

NOT A RACE

DATE

DAILY PLAN

○ Personal Visualisation　　○ Exercise/stretches

○ Personal Development　　○ Helping others

○ Relaxation　　　　　　　　○ Fun/excitement

○ Personal affirmation　　　○ Be grateful

TO DO

○　　　　　　　　　　　　　○

○　　　　　　　　　　　　　○

	URGENT	NON-URGENT
IMPORTANT		
NOT IMPORTANT		

WE ARE SUCH STUFF AS DREAMS ARE MADE ON

THE TEMPEST

DATE

DAILY PLAN

○ **Personal Visualisation** ○ **Exercise/stretches**

○ **Personal Development** ○ **Helping others**

○ **Relaxation** ○ **Fun/excitement**

○ **Personal affirmation** ○ **Be grateful**

TO DO

○ ○

○ ○

	URGENT	NON-URGENT
IMPORTANT		
NOT IMPORTANT		

DON'T REGRET THE PAST

JUST LEARN FROM IT

DATE

DAILY PLAN

○ Personal Visualisation   ○ Exercise/stretches

○ Personal Development   ○ Helping others

○ Relaxation   ○ Fun/excitement

○ Personal affirmation   ○ Be grateful

TO DO

○   ○

○   ○

	URGENT	NON-URGENT
IMPORTANT		
NOT IMPORTANT		

TO BE THE BEST YOU MUST BE ABLE TO HANDLE THE WORST

DATE

DAILY PLAN

- ◯ Personal Visualisation
- ◯ Personal Development
- ◯ Relaxation
- ◯ Personal affirmation

- ◯ Exercise/stretches
- ◯ Helping others
- ◯ Fun/excitement
- ◯ Be grateful

TO DO

- ◯
- ◯

- ◯
- ◯

	URGENT	NON-URGENT
IMPORTANT		
NOT IMPORTANT		

DOUBT KILLS MORE DREAMS THAN FAILURE EVER WILL

DATE

DAILY PLAN

○ Personal Visualisation   ○ Exercise/stretches

○ Personal Development   ○ Helping others

○ Relaxation   ○ Fun/excitement

○ Personal affirmation   ○ Be grateful

TO DO

○   ○

○   ○

	URGENT	NON-URGENT
IMPORTANT		
NOT IMPORTANT		

BE
YOU
AND
STAY
YOU

DATE

DAILY PLAN

○ Personal Visualisation

○ Personal Development

○ Relaxation

○ Personal affirmation

○ Exercise/stretches

○ Helping others

○ Fun/excitement

○ Be grateful

TO DO

○

○

○

○

	URGENT	NON-URGENT
IMPORTANT		
NOT IMPORTANT		

IT IS GOOD PEOPLE WHO MAKE GOOD PLACES

DATE

DAILY PLAN

- ◯ Personal Visualisation
- ◯ Personal Development
- ◯ Relaxation
- ◯ Personal affirmation

- ◯ Exercise/stretches
- ◯ Helping others
- ◯ Fun/excitement
- ◯ Be grateful

TO DO

◯

◯

◯

◯

	URGENT	NON-URGENT
IMPORTANT		
NOT IMPORTANT		

WEEK 1

The aim of this page is to check in with yourself, praise your achievements, reflect on any improvements for the next week and help you achieve your goals.

MY GREATEST ACHIEVEMENT

REFLECTION PAGE

IDEAS FOR IMPROVEMENT NEXT WEEK?

WHAT WAS MY TREAT?

WHAT ARE MY NEXT GOALS?

WELL DONE

HOW DO YOU FEEL?

BE SO GOOD THEY CAN'T IGNORE YOU

DATE

DAILY PLAN

○ Personal Visualisation   ○ Exercise/stretches

○ Personal Development   ○ Helping others

○ Relaxation   ○ Fun/excitement

○ Personal affirmation   ○ Be grateful

TO DO

○   ○

○   ○

	URGENT	NON-URGENT
IMPORTANT		
NOT IMPORTANT		

DO ONE THING EVERY DAY THAT SCARES YOU

DATE

DAILY PLAN

○ **Personal Visualisation**   ○ **Exercise/stretches**

○ **Personal Development**   ○ **Helping others**

○ **Relaxation**   ○ **Fun/excitement**

○ **Personal affirmation**   ○ **Be grateful**

TO DO

○   ○

○   ○

	URGENT	NON-URGENT
IMPORTANT		
NOT IMPORTANT		

LIFE IS ABOUT CREATING YOURSELF

DATE

DAILY PLAN

◯ Personal Visualisation   ◯ Exercise/stretches

◯ Personal Development   ◯ Helping others

◯ Relaxation   ◯ Fun/excitement

◯ Personal affirmation   ◯ Be grateful

TO DO

◯   ◯

◯   ◯

	URGENT	NON-URGENT
IMPORTANT		
NOT IMPORTANT		

OUR THOUGHTS DETERMINE OUR REALITY

DATE

DAILY PLAN

◯ Personal Visualisation   ◯ Exercise/stretches

◯ Personal Development   ◯ Helping others

◯ Relaxation   ◯ Fun/excitement

◯ Personal affirmation   ◯ Be grateful

TO DO

◯   ◯

◯   ◯

	URGENT	NON-URGENT
IMPORTANT		
NOT IMPORTANT		

HOPE
IS THE
ONLY
THING
STRONGER
THAN FEAR

DATE

DAILY PLAN

○ Personal Visualisation   ○ Exercise/stretches

○ Personal Development   ○ Helping others

○ Relaxation   ○ Fun/excitement

○ Personal affirmation   ○ Be grateful

TO DO

○   ○

○   ○

	URGENT	NON-URGENT
IMPORTANT		
NOT IMPORTANT		

MAKE TODAY SO AWESOME THAT YESTERDAY GETS JEALOUS

DATE

DAILY PLAN

○ Personal Visualisation

○ Personal Development

○ Relaxation

○ Personal affirmation

○ Exercise/stretches

○ Helping others

○ Fun/excitement

○ Be grateful

TO DO

○

○

○

○

	URGENT	NON-URGENT
IMPORTANT		
NOT IMPORTANT		

DON'T REGRET THE PAST

JUST LEARN FROM IT

DATE

DAILY PLAN

○ Personal Visualisation   ○ Exercise/stretches

○ Personal Development   ○ Helping others

○ Relaxation   ○ Fun/excitement

○ Personal affirmation   ○ Be grateful

TO DO

○   ○

○   ○

	URGENT	NON-URGENT
IMPORTANT		
NOT IMPORTANT		

WEEK 2

The aim of this page is to check in with yourself, praise your achievements, reflect on any improvements for the next week and help you achieve your goals.

MY GREATEST ACHIEVEMENT

REFLECTION PAGE

IDEAS FOR IMPROVEMENT NEXT WEEK?

WHAT WAS MY TREAT?

WHAT ARE MY NEXT GOALS?

WINNERS ARE NOT PEOPLE WHO NEVER FAIL

BUT PEOPLE WHO NEVER QUIT

DATE

DAILY PLAN

◯ Personal Visualisation　　◯ Exercise/stretches

◯ Personal Development　　◯ Helping others

◯ Relaxation　　　　　　　◯ Fun/excitement

◯ Personal affirmation　　　◯ Be grateful

TO DO

◯　　　　　　　　　　　◯

◯　　　　　　　　　　　◯

	URGENT	NON-URGENT
IMPORTANT		
NOT IMPORTANT		

IF YOU DREAM IT

YOU CAN ACHIEVE IT

DATE

DAILY PLAN

○ Personal Visualisation   ○ Exercise/stretches

○ Personal Development   ○ Helping others

○ Relaxation   ○ Fun/excitement

○ Personal affirmation   ○ Be grateful

TO DO

○   ○

○   ○

	URGENT	NON-URGENT
IMPORTANT		
NOT IMPORTANT		

OUR GREATEST WEAKNESS LIES IN GIVING UP

DATE

DAILY PLAN

○ Personal Visualisation   ○ Exercise/stretches

○ Personal Development   ○ Helping others

○ Relaxation   ○ Fun/excitement

○ Personal affirmation   ○ Be grateful

TO DO

○   ○

○   ○

	URGENT	NON-URGENT
IMPORTANT		
NOT IMPORTANT		

IF YOU DON'T ASK THE ANSWER IS NO

DATE

DAILY PLAN

- ◯ Personal Visualisation
- ◯ Personal Development
- ◯ Relaxation
- ◯ Personal affirmation

- ◯ Exercise/stretches
- ◯ Helping others
- ◯ Fun/excitement
- ◯ Be grateful

TO DO

- ◯
- ◯

- ◯
- ◯

	URGENT	NON-URGENT
IMPORTANT		
NOT IMPORTANT		

ENJOY LIFE NOW

DATE

DAILY PLAN

- ○ Personal Visualisation
- ○ Personal Development
- ○ Relaxation
- ○ Personal affirmation

- ○ Exercise/stretches
- ○ Helping others
- ○ Fun/excitement
- ○ Be grateful

TO DO

- ○
- ○

- ○
- ○

	URGENT	NON-URGENT
IMPORTANT		
NOT IMPORTANT		

NEVER REGRET SOMETHING THAT ONCE MADE YOU SMILE

DATE

DAILY PLAN

○ Personal Visualisation   ○ Exercise/stretches

○ Personal Development   ○ Helping others

○ Relaxation   ○ Fun/excitement

○ Personal affirmation   ○ Be grateful

TO DO

○   ○

○   ○

	URGENT	NON-URGENT
IMPORTANT		
NOT IMPORTANT		

DON'T LET YOUR STRUGGLE BECOME YOUR IDENTITY

DATE

DAILY PLAN

- ◯ Personal Visualisation
- ◯ Personal Development
- ◯ Relaxation
- ◯ Personal affirmation

- ◯ Exercise/stretches
- ◯ Helping others
- ◯ Fun/excitement
- ◯ Be grateful

TO DO

- ◯
- ◯

- ◯
- ◯

	URGENT	NON-URGENT
IMPORTANT		
NOT IMPORTANT		

WEEK 3

The aim of this page is to check in with yourself, praise your achievements, reflect on any improvements for the next week and help you achieve your goals.

MY GREATEST ACHIEVEMENT

REFLECTION PAGE

IDEAS FOR IMPROVEMENT NEXT WEEK?

WHAT WAS MY TREAT?

WHAT ARE MY NEXT GOALS?

POSITIVE THOUGHTS WILL GIVE YOU A POSITIVE LIFE

DATE

DAILY PLAN

○ Personal Visualisation   ○ Exercise/stretches

○ Personal Development   ○ Helping others

○ Relaxation   ○ Fun/excitement

○ Personal affirmation   ○ Be grateful

TO DO

○   ○

○   ○

	URGENT	NON-URGENT
IMPORTANT		
NOT IMPORTANT		

WORRY LESS

SMILE MORE

DATE

DAILY PLAN

○ Personal Visualisation   ○ Exercise/stretches

○ Personal Development   ○ Helping others

○ Relaxation   ○ Fun/excitement

○ Personal affirmation   ○ Be grateful

TO DO

○   ○

○   ○

	URGENT	NON-URGENT
IMPORTANT		
NOT IMPORTANT		

THE MORE YOU
PRAISE AND
CELEBRATE
YOUR LIFE

THE MORE
THERE IS TO
CELEBRATE

DATE

DAILY PLAN

- ◯ Personal Visualisation
- ◯ Personal Development
- ◯ Relaxation
- ◯ Personal affirmation

- ◯ Exercise/stretches
- ◯ Helping others
- ◯ Fun/excitement
- ◯ Be grateful

TO DO

- ◯
- ◯

- ◯
- ◯

	URGENT	NON-URGENT
IMPORTANT		
NOT IMPORTANT		

LIFE IS ABOUT CREATING YOURSELF

DATE

DAILY PLAN

- ◯ Personal Visualisation
- ◯ Personal Development
- ◯ Relaxation
- ◯ Personal affirmation

- ◯ Exercise/stretches
- ◯ Helping others
- ◯ Fun/excitement
- ◯ Be grateful

TO DO

- ◯
- ◯

- ◯
- ◯

	URGENT	NON-URGENT
IMPORTANT		
NOT IMPORTANT		

NEVER STOP

TRYING

LEARNING

EXPERIMENTING

DOING

UNTIL THE MIRACLE HAPPENS

DATE

DAILY PLAN

◯ Personal Visualisation   ◯ Exercise/stretches

◯ Personal Development   ◯ Helping others

◯ Relaxation   ◯ Fun/excitement

◯ Personal affirmation   ◯ Be grateful

TO DO

◯   ◯

◯   ◯

	URGENT	NON-URGENT
IMPORTANT		
NOT IMPORTANT		

YOU CAN NEVER SUCCEED IF YOU DON'T TRY

DATE

DAILY PLAN

○ Personal Visualisation   ○ Exercise/stretches

○ Personal Development   ○ Helping others

○ Relaxation   ○ Fun/excitement

○ Personal affirmation   ○ Be grateful

TO DO

○   ○

○   ○

	URGENT	NON-URGENT
IMPORTANT		
NOT IMPORTANT		

WHEN I LET GO OF WHAT I AM

I BECOME WHAT I MIGHT BE

DATE

DAILY PLAN

- ◯ Personal Visualisation
- ◯ Personal Development
- ◯ Relaxation
- ◯ Personal affirmation

- ◯ Exercise/stretches
- ◯ Helping others
- ◯ Fun/excitement
- ◯ Be grateful

TO DO

◯   ◯

◯   ◯

	URGENT	NON-URGENT
IMPORTANT		
NOT IMPORTANT		

THOUGHTS

SMILE!

WEEK 4

MY GREATEST ACHIEVEMENTS
OVER THE 4 WEEKS

REFLECTION PAGE

MY GREATEST ACHIEVEMENTS
OVER THE 4 WEEKS

MY GREATEST ACHIEVEMENTS
OVER THE 4 WEEKS

PLANS FROM HERE?

Printed in Great Britain
by Amazon